HOME WORKING

101 Everyday Activities in

Social Studies, Media, and Life Skills

The Metropolitan Toronto School Board

Pembroke Publishers Limited

©1996 **The Metropolitan Toronto School Board**
   Pembroke Publishers
   538 Hood Road
   Markham, Ontario, Canada L3R 3K9

Originally prepared cooperatively by and for the Public
School Boards in Metropolitan Toronto under the auspices
of The Metropolitan Toronto School Board.

Project Leader & Writer: Jan Cornwall
Writers: Don Lowrie, Judith Lowther, Paul Stuart,
   Paul Wilson, Beverly Wright
Revisions & Additions: Linda Hart-Hewins,
   Nanci Goldman, Fran Parkin

Canadian Cataloguing in Publication Data

Main entry under title:

101 everyday activities in social studies, media, and life skills

(Homeworking)
ISBN 1-55138-0722

1. Social sciences - Problems, exercises, etc.
2. Life skills - Problems, exercises, etc. 3. Mass
media - Problems, exercises, etc. I. Metropolitan
Toronto School Board. II. Title: One hundred and
one everyday activities in social studies, media,
and life skills. III. Series.

LB1584.054 1996   649'.68   C95-932925-0

Editor: Kate Revington
Cover: John Zehethofer
Illustrations: Jean Taylor
Typesetting: Jay Tee Graphics Ltd.

Printed and bound in Canada by Webcom
9 8 7 6 5 4 3 2

Contents

A Climate for HomeWorking

How much homework do you expect Maria to do each night? I want you to send home some homework for Pedro. Susan needs more homework. What is your homework policy? How can I help Nicole at home?...

Parents often talk to teachers about homework. They **want** their children to do it. They want to help their children at home.

Teachers also see the value of homework. They know from their daily work that the more time students spend on curriculum tasks, the stronger their academic achievement is likely to be. The regular assignment of meaningful homework serves to increase this essential study time.

Homework links home and school both practically and symbolically. It lets parents become involved in the school lives of their children. It can, many parents believe, greatly influence their children's lives and homes. How much or little homework students do, the sort of feedback offered by staff, children's responses to their homework, and the roles parents are expected to play can all affect home life significantly. Such influences need to be positive if homework is to lead to improved academic results.

Good homework, carefully planned, is far more than busywork. In fact, the best homework actively recognizes children's real world. And it calls for the inclusion of children in decisions about where and when they will do the work.

Children do not do homework in a vacuum.

Teachers need to know something about their students' parents. They should find out what their educational backgrounds and interests are. They should also know if the parents' first language is English. If it is not, they will need to take the initiative in translating homework assignments, such as those presented here, into that language.

Similarly, parents may need help in recognizing the many everyday opportunities for teaching their children concepts and skills that complement their school studies. This ***HomeWorking*** book, with its open-ended activities, will help parents to identify many ways they can effectively help their children learn. Parents can not only directly follow activity pages with their children but, in many cases, can take advantage of real-life situations without their children thinking that they are "doing homework."

Whether parents or teachers give homework to children, they need to reinforce one another. Parents and caregivers should turn to teachers for direction and assistance and support their children in doing assigned homework. Conversely, teachers need to supply regular feedback to families.

Judiciously assigned, the quality and quantity of homework can help cement the home-school bond necessary for children's academic achievement and the improved performance of all students.

About the Activities

This book has been designed to assist parents in providing their children with effective homework. The activities are organized for easy use into three main parts, **Personal Development and Skills**, **Social Studies**, and **Media**. They are suitable not only for individual children, but for small and large groups, if teachers adopt them.

Each activity sheet is constructed so that children of all developmental levels can succeed. It provides a list of readily accessible materials necessary for completing the activities and the instructions for doing them.

On each activity sheet, you will note a bullet box that stands alone at the end of Ideas to Talk About. That is an invitation for parents and children to come up with their own authentic questions to explore. Be sure not to overlook the opportunity.

PART 1

Personal Development and Skills

The activities presented here are cross-curricular ones that focus on personal values, life skills, and the home as a centre of learning.

When engaging in life skills activities with your child, try to remember that through everyday experiences, both real and simulated, your child is attempting to gain control over his or her world. Learning to interact successfully with people, objects and events in everyday situations will help your child develop confidence and independence.

The suggested activities reflect that there are many opportunities for meaningful learning to take place at home. Everyday events can take on a whole new meaning when the family shares these opportunities to learn together. When children learn through active participation around the home, they become better prepared to develop into responsible adults.

Counting on You

PURPOSE: Learning the value of honesty

MATERIALS
pencil, paper

ACTIVITIES
❏ Imagine you have bought a chocolate bar and have been given too much change.
❏ Discuss how you would feel and what you would do. Write down your ideas.
❏ Discuss how the cashier would feel.
❏ Discuss how the cashier would react to your actions.

IDEAS TO TALK ABOUT
❏ How would you decide what to do?
❏ How might you feel after you have decided what to do?
❏

Nothing but the Truth

PURPOSE: Learning to make decisions

MATERIALS
Aesop's fable, "The Boy Who Cried Wolf"

ACTIVITIES

You might want to tell rather than read this traditional story.

❑ Read "The Boy Who Cried Wolf" aloud with a partner.

❑ Discuss why the boy told his lies.

❑ Discuss how the townspeople reacted.

IDEAS TO TALK ABOUT

❑ How do people respond when they discover they have been lied to?

❑ How do you feel when someone lies to you?

❑ What alternatives are there to telling lies?

❑

Anticipation

PURPOSE: Using the calendar to record special events

MATERIALS

an old calendar, pencil, ruler, crayons

ACTIVITIES

❑ Make a blank page for a month using a home calendar as a model.

❑ Enter the month and day numbers.

❑ Use the calendar to record special events happening this month, such as birthdays, holidays, school events, celebrations, lessons, and favourite television shows.

❑ Be sure to decorate your personal monthly calendar and keep it handy as a reminder.

IDEAS TO TALK ABOUT

❑ Which months have more than one special event?

❑ What was the name of last month?

❑ How many months is it until...?

❑

11

Choose a Chore

PURPOSE: Learning responsible behaviour

MATERIALS
pencil, paper

ACTIVITIES
❏ Make a list of household chores and who does them.
❏ Decide on responsibilities that could be changed or shared.
❏ Write a list of your suggestions.

IDEAS TO TALK ABOUT
❏ Which chores are daily?
❏ Which chores are weekly?
❏ Are there any chores you would like to learn to do?
❏

Purchasing Power

PURPOSE: Developing awareness of cost and monetary values

MATERIALS
money, a few items that you or your family needs to purchase

ACTIVITIES

Real life is very much an effective teacher!

❏ Go shopping for something that you will pay cash for.

❏ Give the money to the cashier when you are ready to buy the item(s).

❏ Count the change together.

IDEAS TO TALK ABOUT

❏ Are you sure you have enough money to give the cashier? What might happen if you did not?

❏ Are you spending your money wisely? How do you know?

❏ What items could you buy with the change?

❏

Everything Expires

PURPOSE: Learning good consumer habits

MATERIALS

groceries, pencil, paper

ACTIVITIES

❏ Find the expiry date on several food items in the cupboard or refrigerator.

❏ Examine the different ways the date can be written.

❏ Determine how long it is until each product expires.

❏ When shopping for groceries, look at expiry dates together.

❏ Dispose of any expired products you find.

IDEAS TO TALK ABOUT

❏ Which products have a long time before they expire?

❏ Which products have a short time before they expire?

❏ Will you be able to use all of the product before expiry?

❏ Does the expiry date ever affect the price?

❏

14

Let's Get Cooking!

PURPOSE: Learning to plan and organize a meal

MATERIALS
food ingredients, paper, pencil crayons, kitchen utensils, cutlery, plates, cups, table decorations, cookbooks (optional)

ACTIVITIES
Kids can also check and maybe reorganize the cutlery drawer, then set the table for dinner. They'll need to think about which items and how many of each the family will need.

❏ Decide what food you would like to serve for a meal.

❏ Make and decorate a menu to illustrate your planned meal.

❏ Have everyone participate in the preparation, serving, and clean-up.

❏ Celebrate your success.

IDEAS TO TALK ABOUT
❏ Is this a well-balanced, nutritious meal? Why?

❏ Have you considered the likes and dislikes of others?

❏ Have you considered whether there are certain foods people are allergic to?

❏ How can you make sure your meal is a success?

❏

Whipping the Kitchen into Shape

PURPOSE: Appreciating and establishing order and organization in the kitchen

MATERIALS
various kitchen resources, including recipes, stored food, cutlery, plates, and serving dishes

ACTIVITIES
❑ Prepare recipes together.
  • Discuss the effects of low, medium, and high temperatures when cooking.
❑ Make a list of many foods found in your kitchen.
  • Organize your list under the headings Sweet, Salty, Sour, and Bitter.
❑ Make a list of all the items you can buy in packages of two, three, four, six, or eight —weiners, bars of soap, muffins, and so on.

IDEAS TO TALK ABOUT
❑ What changes take place during cooking?
❑ Why is it important to choose the right size of cooking or serving container? What might happen if you didn't?
❑ When might you set extra forks and spoons?
❑ Why do you think some food items, such as muffins and eggs, come in the quantities they do?
❑

Hanging Out at Home

PURPOSE: To become actively aware of the home as an environment.

MATERIALS

pencil, paper, pencil crayons or markers, various household objects, bag

ACTIVITIES

❏ Look at different household systems such as heating, plumbing or electricity. Discuss how they work or draw a picture of your home showing the systems at work.

❏ Reduce, reuse, recycle, repair, and reject in your home.

  • Make a household plan for aiding the environment and follow it daily.

❏ Make a list of all the things you can compost. Ask neighbours for their ideas.

❏ Play Hidden Objects by placing household objects in a bag and having someone guess what each is by touch only.

❏ Have a smell test. Try identifying household objects or safe substances using only your sense of smell.

IDEAS TO TALK ABOUT

❏ What makes your home warm or cool in summer? in winter? Do you find the temperature comfortable?

❏ What makes it easy for you and your family to reduce, reuse, recycle and repair? What makes it more difficult?

❏ How hard is it to identify familiar things using one sense only? Why or why not?

❏

Dangerous Drawings

PURPOSE: Increasing awareness of hazards in the home

MATERIALS
paper, pencil, crayons or markers

ACTIVITIES
❏ Search for and list areas of your home that are dangerous.

❏ Draw a picture of your home that shows the dangers you have listed.

❏ Discuss ways that your family could make these places safer.

❏ Draw warning posters for your home.

IDEAS TO TALK ABOUT
❏ Are there things you could buy or make to increase safety in your home? What are some of those things?

❏ What would you do if you saw someone approaching a dangerous area?

❏

Safety Search

PURPOSE: Understanding product warning labels

MATERIALS
household products, pencil, paper

ACTIVITIES

Parents should be sure to supervise this exploration of hazardous products.

❑ Search for the toxic cleansers, paint supplies and more in your home and garage, if you have one.

❑ Make a list of all of these products.

❑ Beside each product name, draw the product warning label and write what it means.

❑ Discuss household rules for handling these products.

❑ Make a plan for safe storage.

IDEAS TO TALK ABOUT

❑ What can you do to protect yourself?

❑ How can you safely store hazardous products?

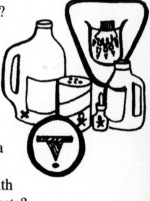

❑ What would you do if you saw a friend or a neighbourhood child playing with hazardous products?

❑

Laundry Labours

PURPOSE: Understanding what is required for the proper care of clothing

MATERIALS

clothing that needs to be laundered, pencil, paper, washing machine, dryer or clothesline, laundry soap

ACTIVITIES

❑ Examine the clothing care labels on shirt and sweater tags. Find out what each symbol means and why it is used for that material.

❑ Make a list of stains found on clothing. Find out ways to reduce or eliminate these stains. Discuss what steps should be taken immediately.

❑ When doing some laundry, read the instructions carefully. Discuss why certain fabrics have different washing and drying instructions.

❑ Fold the laundry. Decide which way to sort the clothes. Talk about your sorting ideas.

IDEAS TO TALK ABOUT

❑ Why must some items of clothing be washed separately? by hand? without bleach?

❑ When is it important to iron clothes?

❑ How should you determine whether to keep wearing something or make it a rag?

❑ Does cleaning clothing make it look older? How?

❑

Time for Action

PURPOSE: Learning to make an emergency call

MATERIALS

pencil, paper, disconnected or play phone

ACTIVITIES

❏ Discuss times when you need to call 911.

❏ Talk about how important this service is and why it should never be misused.

❏ Make a script for a call to 911 and practise it, taking turns as the caller.

❏ Make a list of important family information to be kept by the phone.

IDEAS TO TALK ABOUT

❏ When must you call 911?

❏ How should you behave in such an emergency?

❏

Fire Route

PURPOSE: Planning emergency behaviour

MATERIALS

pencil, paper, markers or crayons, smoke detectors, fire safety brochures

ACTIVITIES

❏ Check that all smoke detectors or carbon monoxide detectors in and around your home are in proper working condition.

❏ Have a family discussion about how you should behave if a fire ever broke out in your home.

❏ Make a fire action plan. Be sure to include routes to the outside and a place to meet.

❏ Practise your fire action plan and discuss how you felt afterwards.

IDEAS TO TALK ABOUT

❏ What would you do if you discovered a fire?

❏ What will you do if you hear a smoke or fire alarm?

❏ What steps can you take to prevent fires?

❏

Street Smart

PURPOSE: Increasing personal safety in your neighbourhood

Your local police force may have brochures or videos on this theme. Sometimes, schools offer streetproofing classes as part of an after school program.

ACTIVITIES

❑ Together, discuss what a child should do if approached by a stranger.

❑ Make a picture of your street showing all of the houses where a child could go in an emergency.

❑ Attend a Block Parents meeting or read together the information available through the school.

❑ Take a walking tour of your neighbourhood to identify safe and unsafe places to play.

IDEAS TO TALK ABOUT

❑ What would you do if a stranger started talking to you?

❑ What neighbours' houses are safe to go to in an emergency?

❑ What would you do if you saw a friend talking to a stranger?

❑

PART 2

Social Studies

Part 2 of this book takes the student beyond himself or herself and the family home and into the wider community.

The cross-curricular activities suggested here recognize that the communities and neighbourhoods where we live can be sources of adventure and learning. A walk to school, lunch at a local restaurant, or a simple stroll in the park present a whole new world of learning opportunities. So too can the travelling that families do for pleasure or business. Families can find sound opportunities for learning by noticing the environment of the community in which they find themselves.

Families can also draw on the familiar to develop knowledge and understanding not only of their own country but of other countries. Food, travel pamphlets, globes or atlases, and more can open up an awareness of the world and its peoples. This awareness can be enhanced through children's experiences and discussions on their own culture, and through comparisons of that culture with the cultures of other people. As children learn more about other cultures, they develop the ability to accept, like, and respect people of different cultures.

Walk About

PURPOSE: Becoming familiar with the patterns in your neighbourhood

MATERIALS
paper, pencil, pencil crayons or markers

ACTIVITIES
❑ Make a list of all area street signs.
  • Put your entries in alphabetical order.
❑ Notice how the buildings on your street are numbered. Determine the pattern.
❑ Make a separate card for each street in your neighbourhood.
  • Arrange the cards in order from the longest to the shortest street.
  • Arrange the cards to show a map of the streets in your neighbourhood.
❑ Draw pictures of area street signs.
  • Write what each one means and discuss the sign's importance.
❑ Plan several walking routes to your neighbourhood store, library or school.
  • Discuss their advantages and disadvantages.
❑ Make a map of your neighbourhood. Be sure to label important places like the school, public library, a friend's house.

IDEAS TO TALK ABOUT
❑ What colour patterns do the signs have? Why do you think the signs have them?
❑ Is the shortest route somewhere always the best? Why or why not?
❑

25

Take a Trip

PURPOSE: To use every sort of trip taken as a learning experience

MATERIALS

pencil, paper, watch, tourist attraction pamphlets

ACTIVITIES

❑ Decide how long it takes for you to go to school or to the nearest store.

• Use a watch to time yourself.

❑ On a trip to the public library, use the computer catalogue to find a book on a topic of interest. You can ask for a librarian's help.

❑ Write a plan for a trip to a local attraction. Discuss what you will see there.

• Once you go, record important things learned.

❑ List all the usual places the family goes—the mall, the zoo, grandma's house, and so on.

• Estimate how far it is to each place; then find the actual distance.

❑ Plan a trip by bus or car.

• Make a timeline for the day showing all important events in sequence.

IDEAS TO TALK ABOUT

❑ How accurate were you in estimating how long it would take to get to a particular place?

❑

Soaking Up Sights and Sounds

PURPOSE: To make a holiday experience vivid and rich in learning

MATERIALS

pencil, paper, pencil crayons or markers, newspapers

ACTIVITIES

You don't need to go anywhere exotic. You can try to look at a familiar place, such as the family cottage or grand-parents' home, in a fresh way.

❏ Read road signs, menus, instructions, brochures, and so on.

❏ Keep a list of new words or phrases that people use on your vacation. Discover whether there are things that you usually say that others find unusual.

• Make a crossword or word search using new words that you have learned.

❏ Buy the local newspaper in different towns and cities and compare it to the one your family reads most at home.

❏ Record the sights and sounds in airports, and train and bus stations.

❏ Sketch and describe the different land-scapes you encounter.

IDEAS TO TALK ABOUT

❏ What is the most unusual sound you have heard?

❏ What is the quietest part of your holiday? the loudest? Why?

❏

No Place like Home

PURPOSE: To reflect on holiday experiences

MATERIALS
pen, paper, pencil crayons or markers, road guide or tourist materials with map, photographs (optional)

ACTIVITIES
❏ Design a postcard to show a beautiful view you saw.
  • Write something about it.
  • Send it to a friend or family relation.
❏ Write a letter to a friend or relative telling your pen pal all about your trip.
❏ Draw pictures of the most enjoyable times of your trip.
❏ If you took any photographs, get them developed. Write what was happening in each picture and put the pictures and your notes in a special album.
❏ Make your own map of the trip you took. Use a road guide or some of the travel flyers you collected to help you.
❏ Interview family members to find out what they most enjoyed doing and why.

IDEAS TO TALK ABOUT
❏ What are the things about home that make you happy to be back? Make a list of them.
❏ What are the similarities between your home and where you have been? What are the differences?
❏

Family Matters

PURPOSE: Relating family history to geographical locations

MATERIALS
a map of the world or a globe or a map of your country

ACTIVITIES
❑ Find cities or countries on a globe or a map where members of your family were born.

❑ Find places where some friends were born.

Recent immigrants may seem to be the most obvious candidates for doing these activities. However the activities can apply equally well to families who have moved within one country or even one city.

IDEAS TO TALK ABOUT
❑ If your family comes from somewhere else, what was life like there?

❑ How did some of your family or friends come to live where you are now?

❑ Which members of your family still live in the place where your family originated?

❑ How is life here different for your family?

❑

Wave the Flag

PURPOSE: Becoming familiar with your national flag

MATERIALS

paper or cloth material, scissors, glue, straws or sticks, a picture of the national flag

ACTIVITIES

❏ Look at a picture of the national flag.

❏ Make your own flag with paper or cloth material.

❏ Glue the flag to a straw or stick.

❏ Make flags for any other countries that members of your family came from recently or some time in the past.

IDEAS TO TALK ABOUT

❏ What does the flag symbolize?

❏ How old is the flag design? Do some research.

❏ What other flags has the country used?

❏ Does your local or regional community have a flag? What does it look like?

❏

From Sea to Sea

PURPOSE: Learning about your own country's political divisions

MATERIALS
atlas, pencil, index cards

ACTIVITIES
❏ Together, find a map of your country in an atlas.

❏ Locate each major political division, for example, provinces, and record its name on a separate index card.

❏ Scramble the index cards for each other.

❏ Choose an index card and find the place identified on your map.

❏ Make a crossword puzzle using the names identified on the index cards.

IDEAS TO TALK ABOUT
❏ Which city is the nation's capital? Where is it?

❏ Which of the names you have recorded do you think is the most unusual? Why?

❏ Which name do you like best? Why?

❏ Which name is the longest? the shortest?

❏

Places We Know

PURPOSE: Identifying various places in your country

MATERIALS

atlas, map showing your country

ACTIVITIES

You can also ask kids where in the country they would like to visit and have them find these places on an appropriate map.

❏ Look on the map to find places in your country where you have lived or visited.

❏ Look on the map to find places where family or friends live.

❏ Consider what you know about these places.

IDEAS TO TALK ABOUT

❏ Can you find more information about some of these places from family or library books? What else would you like to know?

❏ How far is it to some of these places?

❏ What would you experience in some of these places?

❏

Where Have You Been?

PURPOSE: Identifying places on a world map

MATERIALS
globe or map of the world

ACTIVITIES
❏ Find the names and locations of countries where you have lived or visited.

❏ Find countries where some of your family or friends are living now.

❏ Ask relatives or friends to point out places they have been.

❏ Ask how these places differ from and how they are like your country.

IDEAS TO TALK ABOUT
❏ What do you know about these places?

❏ What information about some of these places can you get from family or library books?

❏ Which places would you like to visit?

❏ How far is it to some of these places?

❏ Have you travelled most within your own country? Why or why not?

❏

Special Times

PURPOSE: Learning about customs and traditions

MATERIALS

magazines, travel booklets, books, pencil, paper

ACTIVITIES

❏ Make a list of special times that are traditionally celebrated in your country.

❏ Ask a friend with recent roots in another country about special times there.

❏ Draw pictures about special times in your friend's original country.

IDEAS TO TALK ABOUT

❏ What special times are similar to those in your native or adopted country?

❏ Are there special foods or customs for the special times in your friend's original country? What are they?

❏ What special customs would you like to share with your friend?

❏

National News

PURPOSE: Learning about another country

MATERIALS

atlas, travel pamphlets, library books, pencil, paper

ACTIVITIES

❏ Choose a country that you are interested in or about which you can interview reliably.

❏ Find the country on a world map.

❏ Interview someone from that country. Ask about

- clothing
- food
- activities
- land forms
- special occasions

❏ Make a booklet to share at school.

IDEAS TO TALK ABOUT

❏ How far is the country from where you live?

❏ What activities are special to that country?

❏ What similarities and differences do you notice?

❏

More Than Meat and Potatoes

PURPOSE: Developing awareness of the main food groups

MATERIALS
food in the kitchen, paper, pencil

ACTIVITIES
❑ Make lists of some of the food in the kitchen under the headings of Meat, Dairy Products, Fruit and Vegetables, Breads and Cereals.

❑ Make lists to show foods from other countries under each heading.

❑ Include the name of the country.

IDEAS TO TALK ABOUT
❑ How often do you eat each kind of food?

❑ Which kinds of food do you like best?

❑ Which foods are served hot? Which are served cold?

❑

Where in the World...

PURPOSE: Learning about imported foods

MATERIALS
pencil, paper, pencil crayons or markers

ACTIVITIES
❑ Examine cans and boxes of food in your kitchen.

❑ Look on each label to find where the food was produced.

❑ Make a list of each food and its country of origin.

❑ Find the place of origin on a map of the world.

❑ Draw pictures to illustrate your list, or choose one food and draw a picture showing that food growing.

IDEAS TO TALK ABOUT
❑ What foods come from other countries?

❑ Which foods travel a long way to get here?

❑ Which foods from other countries also grow here?

❑

To Market, to Market

PURPOSE: Learning about imported foods

MATERIALS
grocery store, pencil, paper, map of the world

ACTIVITIES
❑ Look for grocery store signs that tell where foods come from.

❑ List each food along with its country of origin.

❑ When you get home, find each country on a map of the world.

IDEAS TO TALK ABOUT
❑ Which countries send this country the most food?

❑ Why does this country need food from other countries?

❑ Do some foods come only in certain seasons?

❑

Mmmm Good!

PURPOSE: Researching foods from other countries

MATERIALS
Yellow Pages, pencil, paper

ACTIVITIES

If anyone in the family has food allergies, for example, to peanuts, be sure to check out what ingredients are used.

❑ Look in the Yellow Pages of the telephone book for different types of restaurants and record their names.

❑ Locate restaurants in your neighbourhood that serve foods from other countries.

❑ Visit one of these restaurants for a family meal.

❑ Ask restaurant workers what foods to try.

IDEAS TO TALK ABOUT

❑ What special ways are foods cooked?

❑ What special ingredients are used?

❑ How long does food preparation take?

❑

The Sporting Life

PURPOSE: Learning about sports around the world

MATERIALS
magazines, newspapers, pencil, paper

ACTIVITIES
❏ Make a list of as many sports as possible. Get friends and relatives to help.

❏ Beside each sport name, write the countries that play that sport.

❏ Illustrate your research and bring it to school for sharing.

IDEAS TO TALK ABOUT
❏ Which countries play the same sports as your country?

❏ Do some countries have a national sport? What is it?

❏ Which sports are played in many countries?

❏

PART 3

Media

Children spend much time watching television and videos, and listening to CDs and audio tapes. This time can be used to develop viewing, listening, discussion and decision-making skills.

Learning to watch television wisely requires supervision. When families and children view programs together, the child can learn

- ways of managing time wisely;
- how to evaluate and value programs;
- the effects and purposes of commercials;
- social values;
- appreciation for the artistic and technical elements of television.

Beyond often quite justified parental concerns about what their children are watching, teachers deal with children who seem increasingly moulded by the visions, values, and ideas that television presents. Parents and teachers who actively help shape children's viewing habits will allow children to deal effectively with this powerful form of communication.

Paying the Piper

PURPOSE: Discussing feelings about television commercials

MATERIALS
pencil, paper, crayons or markers

ACTIVITIES
❏ Together, choose a television commercial.
❏ Discuss what the commercial wants you to believe, do, or buy.
❏ Determine how the characters in the commercial try to convince you.
❏ Consider whether they are successful. Why or why not?

IDEAS TO TALK ABOUT
❏ What is this commercial trying to do?
❏ How does this commercial make you feel?
❏ How does it make you feel that way?
❏

Alluring Images

PURPOSE: Determining lifestyle influences in commercials

MATERIALS
pencil, paper

ACTIVITIES
❏ Together, watch a television program.

❏ Each time a commercial break occurs, turn the sound off.

❏ For each commercial, print the name of the product and list everything you see in the commercial.

❏ Determine to whom these commercials are directed.

❏ Decide which group of people would buy this product.

IDEAS TO TALK ABOUT
❏ What pictures or images are used to sell the product?

❏ Who is most likely to buy this product?

❏ Why have these images been chosen for this commercial?

❏

Sheep or Wolves?

PURPOSE: Identifying positive and negative influences

MATERIALS
pencil, paper, crayons or markers

ACTIVITIES
❏ View a program together.

❏ List characters as good or evil.

❏ Beside the characters' names, write how you could tell who was good and who was evil.

❏ Draw a picture each of the best and worst characters.

IDEAS TO TALK ABOUT
❏ How can you figure out if a character is good or evil?

❏ Did good and evil have different sounds? What were they?

❏ What would you say if you met one of the characters?

❏

The Trouble with TV

PURPOSE: Identifying positive and negative influences

MATERIALS
pencil, paper

ACTIVITIES
❏ View a program together.
❏ Decide on one thing that you could learn from the program.
❏ Discuss whether this is a good or bad thing to learn.
❏ Together, write a list of good and bad things that television can teach us.

IDEAS TO TALK ABOUT
❏ Is everything on television true? How do you know?
❏ How can you tell what's true from what's false?
❏ What changes would you make to this program?
❏

Product Pushers

PURPOSE: Understanding the purpose of commercials

MATERIALS

pencil, paper, crayons or markers

ACTIVITIES

❏ Watch several commercials together.

❏ Discuss how the advertiser tries to convince you to purchase a product.

❏ Discuss how a person should decide to purchase a product.

❏ Make a list of things to think about pertaining to commercials.

❏ Draw a picture of how you would advertise a product.

IDEAS TO TALK ABOUT

❏ Do you need this product? Why?

❏ Should you purchase this product?

❏ How would you advertise this product?

❏

Reviewing Viewing Habits

PURPOSE: Examining viewing habits

MATERIALS
pencil, paper

ACTIVITIES
❑ Make a television questionnaire about favourite shows, time of day, and length of the program.

❑ Ask several family members, adults, friends, schoolmates to fill it in.

❑ Make a list of favourite shows and how many people chose each program.

IDEAS TO TALK ABOUT
❑ What times are the popular programs on?

❑ How old are the people who watch each program?

❑ What would happen if the program was on at a different time?

❑

Who, What, When?

PURPOSE: Recording viewing habits

MATERIALS
television listings, paper, pencil

ACTIVITIES
❑ Read through the television listings together.

❑ Decide how much television is allowed for you each day.

❑ Make a personal list of day, time, and program for the week.

❑ Follow your agreed-upon list for one week.

❑ Plan next week's viewing in the same manner.

IDEAS TO TALK ABOUT
❑ What types of programs should you watch together? Why?

❑ Who should choose the programs? Why?

❑ Is your way of choosing programs fair?

❑

Fact or Fiction?

PURPOSE: Distinguishing fact from fiction

MATERIALS

television listings, pencil, paper

ACTIVITIES

❏ Choose a documentary program such as *National Geographic, Untamed World* or *Undersea Odyssey.*

❏ View the program together.

❏ Discuss the purpose of the program.

❏ Make a list of things learned from the program.

❏ Discuss whether the content of this program is true or not.

IDEAS TO TALK ABOUT

❏ How are documentary programs paid for?

❏ What can you do to learn more about this topic?

❏ How can you tell if something is true or not true?

❏

Really Popular

PURPOSE: Distinguishing fact from fiction

MATERIALS
pencil, paper

ACTIVITIES
❏ Choose a popular television program to view together.

❏ View the program together.

❏ Discuss the program before it starts, during the commercial breaks, and after it is over.

❏ Decide whether or not the content of the program seemed or was real.

❏ Record how you made your decision.

IDEAS TO TALK ABOUT
❏ What was the story about? Was it believable? Why?

❏ Why do you think this program is popular?

❏ How can you tell if the story is true or not?

❏ What story would you tell on television if you had the chance?

❏

Active Alternatives

PURPOSE: Using family time in positive ways

MATERIALS

pencil, paper, whatever alternative to television you choose

ACTIVITIES

❏ Imagine your television set is broken.

❏ Make a list of activities you could do instead of watching television. Let everyone add to the list.

❏ As a family, decide which activities would be the most fun to do together.

❏ Pick an evening to try one of your alternatives to television.

IDEAS TO TALK ABOUT

❏ What things do you enjoy doing besides watching television?

❏ What could you do if your television was broken?

❏ How did you feel about your evening without television?

❏

These activities may seem to presuppose that all families regularly watch television. Even if your family does not do so daily, you can still apply the activities to the time of heaviest normal television use.

Television Takeoffs

PURPOSE: Developing creative writing skills

MATERIALS
pencil, paper

ACTIVITIES
❑ Watch an episode of a favourite program.
❑ After it is over, discuss what you think will happen next.
❑ Write a story based on your discussion.
❑ Change your story into a script.
❑ Read your script aloud, letting family members take turns reading different parts.

IDEAS TO TALK ABOUT
❑ How did the characters feel at the end of the program?

❑ What would you want to happen next?
❑ What characters would you change if you could?
❑

Visual Violence

PURPOSE: Understanding the impact of violence and choosing alternatives

MATERIALS
pencil, paper

ACTIVITIES

If, as a parent, you would not feel comfortable about exposing your child to such a show, you can apply the activities to a cartoon instead.

❏ Watch a police or other action drama.

❏ Discuss the role of violence in such a program.

❏ Decide how important violence is to these shows.

❏ Discuss which characters are the most violent.

❏ Write a television episode that does not have violence.

IDEAS TO TALK ABOUT

❏ What would happen if violence was banned from television?

❏ Is the violence real or fake? How do you know?

❏

Television Types

PURPOSE: Sorting and classifying television programs

MATERIALS
television listings, pencil, paper

ACTIVITIES
❏ Discuss types of programs that you find in the television listings or like to watch.

❏ Decide on category headings, such as drama, cartoon, comedy, and so on.

❏ Put your headings on a piece of paper.

❏ As you go through the television listings, write the name of each program in the appropriate category.

❏ Compare your lists to see which are the most popular.

IDEAS TO TALK ABOUT
❏ What types of television programs do you watch?

❏ What other types of programs are there? Why don't you watch them?

❏

Fighting at Play

PURPOSE: Identifying violence in sports

MATERIALS

television listings, pencil, paper

ACTIVITIES

❏ Using the television listings, write down all the sports that you can find.

❏ Group them under the headings of Violent and Non-Violent.

❏ Discuss which sports are the most popular.

❏ Invent a new sport and decide the rules for it.

IDEAS TO TALK ABOUT

❏ Which sports seem to rely on violence for popularity?

❏ Does violence make a sport more or less attractive? Why?

❏ What would happen if violence was banned from all sports?

❏

Play by Play

PURPOSE: Analysing differences in media coverage

MATERIALS
television, radio

ACTIVITIES
❏ Listen to a sports program on the radio.

❏ Watch the same sport on television.

❏ Discuss the differences in how the game is announced.

❏ Turn the sound off on the television, and try listening to the game on the radio while watching the television.

❏ Discuss the effect of this change.

IDEAS TO TALK ABOUT
❏ Which announcer provides more detail?

❏ How are commercials different on radio and television?

❏ What comments are most important to you?

❏

Interesting Interviews

PURPOSE: Developing questioning and response skills

MATERIALS
pencil, paper

ACTIVITIES
❏ Watch several programs where people are interviewed.

❏ Make note of the types of questions that are asked.

❏ Choose a famous person that you would like to interview and write a list of questions you would like answered.

❏ Role-play your interview with a family member.

❏ Take turns asking the questions.

IDEAS TO TALK ABOUT
❏ If you could interview anyone in the world, who would you choose?

❏ Why would you choose that person?

❏ What questions would you ask?

❏

Priority Poster

PURPOSE: Presenting information in an attractive format

MATERIALS
pencil, paper, crayons or markers

ACTIVITIES
❏ Select your favourite television program.
❏ Design a poster to advertise that program. Don't forget important information.
❏ Colour your poster and give it a title.
❏ Put your poster up for others to see.

IDEAS TO TALK ABOUT
❏ What are the date, time, and channel of your favourite program?

❏ Where would be a good place to display your poster?
❏ What would you do if your favourite program were cancelled?
❏

Audio Advertising

PURPOSE: Developing writing and dramatic skills

MATERIALS
pencil, paper, tape recorder

ACTIVITIES
❏ Pick a program you wish to advertise.

❏ Listen to radio and television advertisements.

❏ Select background music for your advertisement.

❏ Write a script including all important information.

❏ Record your advertisement and share it with friends or classmates.

IDEAS TO TALK ABOUT
❏ What is the best background music to use?

❏ Whose voices could you use for your advertisement?

❏ Where will you share your advertisement?

❏

Making Ratings

PURPOSE: Gaining information about audiences

MATERIALS
pencil, paper

ACTIVITIES
❏ Take a trip to your local video rental store.
❏ Write down all of the ratings that you can find. For example: General, Adult, Family, PG-13.
❏ List the ratings and write what each means.
❏ Discuss which categories each family member may watch.
❏ Design your own set of ratings for television programs.

IDEAS TO TALK ABOUT
❏ Which ratings are appropriate for children?
❏ How is the rating given to each movie?
❏ What would you do if someone tried to show you a video that you knew you weren't allowed to watch?
❏

Video View

PURPOSE: Classifying videos

MATERIALS
pencil, paper

ACTIVITIES
❏ Make a list of all of the videos or television movies your family has watched recently.

❏ Decide on categories such as family, action, animation, drama, horror, and mystery.

❏ Put each of the videos rented or movies watched into a category.

❏ As you watch more movies, add them to your lists.

IDEAS TO TALK ABOUT
❏ Do some movies fit more than one category? Why?

❏ Why are films and videos longer than regular television programs?

❏ Who decides which movies you watch? Why?

❏

From a Distance

PURPOSE: Developing good viewing habits

MATERIALS
tape measure or metre stick, pencil, paper

ACTIVITIES
❏ Measure the distance that you and others in your home usually sit from the television.

❏ List your measurements from least to greatest.

❏ Adjust your seating to make sure everyone sits at least 1.5 metres (5 ft.) from the screen.

IDEAS TO TALK ABOUT
❏ What could happen if you sit too close to the television?

❏ How far away can you sit and still see comfortably?

❏ Who might have a special reason to sit close? Why?

❏

Television Time

PURPOSE: Recording time spent watching television

MATERIALS
pencil, paper, television watching averages

ACTIVITIES
❑ Guess how many hours each member of your family spends watching television in one week. Include yourself.

❑ Keep a log of television viewing time for one week.

❑ Compare your time with that of friends and family.

❑ Compare results with these averages provided by A.C. Nielsen Co., 1990:
  • average time per week for ages 2-5: 27 hours, 49 minutes
  • average time per week for ages 6-11: 23 hours, 39 minutes

IDEAS TO TALK ABOUT
❑ How does your viewing time compare to the averages?

❑ Should you watch more or less television? Why?

❑ How do your results compare to those of your friends?

❑

Newsmaker Knowledge

PURPOSE: Collecting and analysing information

MATERIALS
television, newspaper, pencil, paper

ACTIVITIES
❏ Watch the news on television, or read a newspaper.

❏ Write the name of a person in the news.

❏ List the reasons why the person was in the news.

❏ Decide what the newsmaker might be like from what you have learned.

IDEAS TO TALK ABOUT
❏ Before today, did you know anything about the person in the news? What?

❏ What would be interesting to find out about that person?

❏ What questions would you like to ask the newsmaker?

❏

Radio Active

PURPOSE: Finding out information from the radio

MATERIALS
radio, globe or atlas, pencil, paper

ACTIVITIES
❏ Listen to the local news and the world news on the radio.

❏ Write the names of countries mentioned and identify the events taking place in those countries.

❏ Use a globe or an atlas to find some of the places talked about on the radio.

IDEAS TO TALK ABOUT
❏ How far from home are some of these places?

❏ What is happening there?

❏ Are similar events taking place in your country?

❏ What kind of news do you think radio presents best?

❏

Nations on News Clips

PURPOSE: Finding out information from television

MATERIALS
television, globe or atlas, pencil, paper

ACTIVITIES

You can also adapt this set of activities to a daily newspaper.

❏ Watch the local news and the world news on television.

❏ Write the names of countries mentioned and identify the events taking place in those countries.

❏ Use a globe or an atlas to find some of the places talked about on television.

IDEAS TO TALK ABOUT

❏ What is happening in some of these places?

❏ How far from your home are the places?

❏ What problems do various countries have?

❏ What else do you know about these places?

❏ What do you think will happen because of what you just saw on television?

❏

Evaluation

It is a good idea for families to review what they have learned from the activities in this book. Doing so will permit them to reinforce that learning and to develop another important skill, reflection. The evaluation forms that follow will promote reflection, or thinking about the learning. Families can also use them to let the school know how what kids are doing at home is supporting what is happening in the classroom.

Families can do both process and summative evaluation. That means they can assess what and how they are learning while they are in the thick of activities; also, at the end of a section or book, they can determine what learning has occurred.

There are three focuses for evaluation.

Family/Child: Many of the Ideas to Talk About will provide focus for ongoing observations and evaluations. These forms can let families discuss and reflect on their shared learning.

Family: Teachers can use these evaluation forms to get valuable feedback. The ideas they get can aid their future planning. Teachers may want to suggest the best evaluation form for specific activities.

School: Parents and teachers can keep an ongoing record of activities done to help them assess *HomeWorking*'s impact on children's learning at school, on the increase of family/school communication, and on their increase of support for both the children and the classroom program.

Names _____ **Date** _____

_____

What we did...	_What we learned..._	_How we felt about it..._

Parent's Name _____ **Date** _____

Activity _____

What materials did you use?

_____

_____

_____

What did you do?

_____

_____

_____

What did your child learn?

_____

_____

_____

What other ideas did you think of?

_____

_____

_____

Parent's Name _____ **Date** _____

Name of Activity

	Not very good	Good	Excellent

_____ ☐   ☐   ☐

_____ ☐   ☐   ☐

_____ ☐   ☐   ☐

_____ ☐   ☐   ☐

_____ ☐   ☐   ☐

Comments

_____

_____

_____

_____

_____

_____

_____

Names _____ **Date** _____

_____

Purpose of Activity _____

Did this activity help your child understand the idea identified above?

☐ *Yes*   ☐ *No*

Comments: _____

_____

_____

_____

Were the instructions clear?

☐ *Yes*   ☐ *No*

Comments: _____

_____

_____

_____

Was your child interested in this activity?

☐ *Yes*   ☐ *No*

Comments: _____

_____

_____

_____

Did this activity stimulate discussion?

☐ *Yes*   ☐ *No*

Comments: _____

_____

_____

_____

Names _____ **Date** _____

_____

Approximate Number of Activities Used _____

Objective   *Level of Understanding*

Helped children
realize that
learning is
ongoing

☐ Beginning   ☐ Fair   ☐ Considerable

Comments: _____

_____

Provided
opportunities
to develop
a closer
relationship

☐ Beginning   ☐ Fair   ☐ Considerable

Comments: _____

_____

Permitted
children to
acquire
new information

☐ Beginning   ☐ Fair   ☐ Considerable

Comments: _____

_____

Permitted
children to
gain new skills

☐ Beginning   ☐ Fair   ☐ Considerable

Comments: _____

_____

Provided
enjoyment

☐ Beginning   ☐ Fair   ☐ Considerable

Comments: _____

_____